Take the

To Barbara

Take the
IQ Challenge

A MENSA BOOK OF PUZZLES

Philip J. Carter

JAVELIN BOOKS
LONDON · NEW YORK · SYDNEY

First published in the UK 1986 by Javelin Books,
Artillery House, Artillery Row, London SW1P 1RT
Reprinted 1986
Reprinted 1987 (twice)
Reprinted 1988
Reprinted 1989

Distributed in the United States by
Sterling Publishing Co., Inc.,
2 Park Avenue, New York, NY 10016

Distributed in Australia by
Capricorn Link (Australia) Pty Ltd,
PO Box 665, Lane Cove, NSW 2066

British Library Cataloguing in Publication Data

Carter, Philip J.
 Take the IQ challenge : A Mensa book of puzzles.
 1. Puzzles
 I. Title
 793.73   GV1493

ISBN 0 7137 1736 X

Typeset in 9/10 Monophoto Ehrhardt by
Latimer Trend & Company Ltd, Plymouth

Printed and bound in Great Britain by
Hazell Watson & Viney Limited
Member of BPCC plc
Aylesbury, Bucks, England

CONTENTS

ACKNOWLEDGEMENTS

I wish to thank the British Mensa Committee for their backing, and Mensa's Executive Director, Harold Gale, for his assistance. Special thanks are due to my wife Barbara for her indispensable help with preparation of the manuscript, correction of mistakes and for her eternal optimism. Last, but not least, I have to thank Ken Russell for suggesting this book to me in the first place, and then for his subsequent words of encouragement and many helpful comments.

I am grateful to all the above for making this book possible.

INTRODUCTION

When the opportunity to produce a puzzle book presented itself to me I was delighted to respond positively. After all, I find puzzles a fascinating hobby, and since joining Mensa in 1983 had become a member of Enigmasig, a Special Interest Group (SIG) within Mensa devoted to the setting and solving of puzzles. Later I had the pleasure of accepting an invitation to become co-editor of the Enigmasig monthly newsletter. Enigmasig is one of about forty Special Interest Groups within Mensa which devote themselves to such varied subjects as philosophical discussion to practical conservation, *Blake's 7* to Richard III, and croquet to chess.

Mensa itself is a unique society where the only criterion for membership is to have achieved an 'IQ' within the top 2 per cent of the population in a supervised 'IQ' test. The qualifying figure is 148 and in theory one person in fifty of the population should qualify for membership. Being the only criterion for membership this means that every member is equally qualified; in fact the name Mensa itself is a Latin word meaning 'table', implying a round table society where no-one has special preference.

As it draws members from a very wide spectrum of the community, Mensa itself neither expresses nor holds any political or religious views. Indeed, being a round table society with such a diverse membership, it would be impossible for it to do so. Members of a like mind are, however, free to group together to form SIGs devoted to a special interest or opinion, but are not allowed to express opinions as being of Mensa itself.

Should anyone be considering applying for membership, I am sure that, if successful, they will find in Mensa a society which will in some way enrich their lives either through the pages of the excellent Journal, through social contact with other members or through one of the many SIGs. Indeed, if there is not already a group within Mensa to suit a particular member's needs he or she is encouraged to start a new group to attract other members of a like mind.

This brings me back to Enigmasig, which caters for my current passion—puzzles. It is a group of about a hundred members with addresses from Fort William to Yelverton, and the object is to compile puzzles to confound and entertain other members. It is from my involvement with Enigmasig that this book has evolved. I have tried to include as wide a selection of different types of puzzles as possible, and of varying degrees of difficulty, and I hope there will be something to interest everyone. The majority of Mensa tests are tests of intelligence rather than of specific general knowledge. Many of the puzzles in this book are also purely intelligence problems, but others, particularly in the 'Categorise' and 'Theme' sections, rely on general knowledge. *A star rating has been given for each puzzle, so that you can monitor your performance:*

    * = hard;
   ** = harder;
*** = hardest.

Please enjoy the puzzles, but do not be in too much of a hurry to look at the answers. If you use your imagination, do not always look for the obvious, and put your mind to work, I think you will be able to come up with many of the right answers, but above all I hope you will find the book an interesting and entertaining diversion.

SEQUENCES AND RELATIONSHIPS

Sequences have been chosen for the first group of puzzles, as they are a great way of sharpening up the mind. With one exception, no specific general knowledge is required, but what is necessary is to analyse and identify logical patterns or relationships between words, numbers or diagrams and decide what should follow, either to continue or to complete the sequence, or alternatively decide what, most appropriately, will match the given list.

In the grids, sequences of numbers, which would be familiar if written out conventionally, are made much trickier by converting them into number mazes.

Find the Sequence

There is a logical way to get from the top left-hand square to the bottom right by moving from square to square horizontally, vertically or diagonally and visiting every square once only. What is it?

START

3	6	5	3	5	9
7	9	1	6	8	0
2	8	1	6	4	9
1	7	8	9	7	1
2	2	4	1	1	7
9	7	3	2	4	7

FINISH

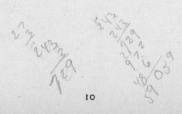

Find the pair to complete the following sequence.

Choose from:

   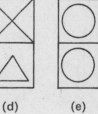

(a)   (b)   (c)   (d)   (e)

In each of the following, find the number which should logically come next in sequence:

  *(a)   266,   196,   256,   169,   ?

  **(b)   126,   72,   648,   512,   9216,   1472,   ?

  ***(c)   Consider the number 864. Now complete the following sequence:

       52,   54,   72,   76,   94,   ?

Travel out of the number maze by finding a meaningful route, starting at the middle square and moving to the top right from square to square horizontally, vertically or diagonally and visiting every square once only.

1	1	5	1	3	OUT
1	7	3	4	4	
3	2	*	3	7	
1	1	2	2	3	
7	9	9	3	1	

*(a)   Find the next letter in this sequence:

TFSETTFSETTTT

***(b)   Find the next most suitable letter:

A, H, I, M

Choose from:

N, P, Q, R, T, V, X

***(c)   Find the next most suitable letter:

F, G, J, L

Choose from:

N, P, S, V, W, Y

In each of the following choose a word which you think will best match the rest.

**(a) AGE,   DATE,   KIND,   FULLY,   POWER

Choose one from:

RAP,   STRUT,   BULLY,   HOOD,   CRIME, YEAR

**(b) HINT,   DIRT,   COSY,   FORT

Choose one from:

KNOT,   PART,   EPIC,   ROUT,   NAVY

*(c) MANOEUVRING,   CAULIFLOWER, ACCENTUATION,   BEHAVIOURISM, GREGARIOUS

Choose one from:

MANUSCRIPT,   CAUTIONED, MATRICULATION,   OBSTREPEROUS, REORIENTATION

Find the next most appropriate square.

Choose from:

(a)   (b)   (c)   (d)   (e)   (f)

Symbolism

Find the next drawing.

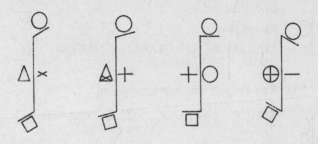

Choose from:

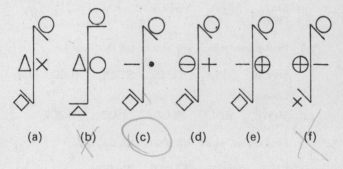

(a)   (b)   (c)   (d)   (e)   (f)

*(a)   Find the next in sequence:

PINT,   QUART,   GALLON,   PECK,
BUSHEL,   ?

Choose from:

CHALDRON,   HECTARE,   QUARTER,
LOAD,   MYRIAGRAM

**(b)   Find the next most appropriate word:

SIRIUS,   NEPTUNE,   ASIA,   FRANCE,
TEXAS,   ?

Choose from:

MAN,   AREA,   SWEDEN,   PACIFIC,
DUBLIN,   CHINA

*(c)   Find a word which will best match this list:

MOOR,   STEP,   TIME,   STAR,   REED,   ?

Choose from:

MOVE,   MOLD,   TUBA,   PACE,   HOUR

**(d)   Find a word which will best match this list:

VICE,   BODY,   TABLE,   WHERE,   ?

Choose from:

CHAIR,   ARM,   HEAD,   MAD,   LEER

Circles

Find the next circle.

Choose from:

(a)   (b)   (c)   (d)   (e)

THEMES

As a contrast to the previous chapter good general knowledge is the main requirement here rather than logic. Each puzzle covers a different theme, sometimes specified, but sometimes left for you to discover by studying, or solving, the clues given.

One of the puzzles proves that Mensa members are dedicated puzzle solvers and will even provide answers which you did not know existed. When the 'Feathered Friends' puzzle (15) appeared in the *Mensa Journal* I asked for the names of twenty birds to be uncovered in the grid. Not only did some members find all twenty, they came up with no fewer than twelve additional birds which I hadn't spotted even though I had compiled the puzzle!

Composers

Fill in the composers below. The marked letters are an anagram of one of the composers' works.

1.　　– A – H – A – I – O –

2.　　– O – N – D

3.　　– C – U – A – N

4.　　– E – T – O – E –

5.　　– L – A –

6.　　– I – E –

7.　　– S – H – I – O – S – Y

8.　　– A – C – G – I

9.　　– C – U – E – T

10.　　– E – D – L – S – H –

11.　　– E – E – B – E –

12.　　– E – L – O –

13.　　– U – C – N –

14.　　– T – A – I – S – Y

15.　　– A – N – R

An Abbreviated World History 1190BC to AD1720

(All in chronological order.)

THE T.W. *rojan* *ar*

D. OF A. THE G. AT B. *reat*

eazi *lexander*

R. I. OF B.

R. OF B. *Rise of*

THE D. A.

THE N.C. OF E.

M.C.S. BY K.J.

THE M.P.

THE H.Y.W.

THE R. OF W.T.

THE B. OF A.

J. OF A. B. AT R.

W. OF THE R.E. BY B. OF B.

C.C.D.A.

S.F.D.S.R.W.

THE G.P.

C.W. IN E.

O.C.B.L.P.

G.F. OF L.

A. OF P. THE G. OF R.

U. OF E. AND S.

THE S.S.B.

Countries

Fill in the countries below. The first letter of each country is an anagram of another country and its capital.

1. A N T I Q U A
2. – A – T – N – Q – E
3. – E – C – E – L – S
4. – U – A –
5. – G – N – A
6. – E – E –
7. – U – A –
8. – L – E – I –
9. – N – O – A
10. – N – O – E – I –
11. – E – E – A –
12. – O – O – B – A
13. – W – N – A

Oxymorons

What is an oxymoron? The answer is a very rarely used word describing a very often used figure of speech in which two words of opposite meaning are linked together to form a descriptive phrase, e.g. golfers play with metal woods and make good bad shots, and snooker players sometimes thin the ball too thickly.

The following is my compilation of oxymorons. Column two has been mixed up and should be paired with a word in column one.

1.	Fine	History
2.	Dry	Permanent Secretary
3.	Awfully	Jump
4.	Slipped	The rear
5.	Sweet	Chilli
6.	Good	Games
7.	Stand	Sherry
8.	Standing	Good
9.	Retired	Goods
10.	Future	Grief
11.	Sit	Fit
12.	War	Beginners
13.	Spend	Sweet
14.	Perfectly	Drizzle
15.	Advance to	Numb
16.	Advanced	Thrift
17.	Feeling	Awful
18.	Bitter	Down
19.	Loose	Up
20.	Hot	Sorrow
21.	Bad	Up

Feathered Friends

By moving from square to square horizontally, vertically or diagonally it is possible to find the names of 32 birds in the grid below. Squares may be used more than once but not in the same name. There are no redundant squares.

N	I	O	L	N	I	W	I
I	O	R	C	E	D	R	N
B	K	U	E	G	R	T	G
O	C	T	N	W	A	R	O
R	R	J	N	I	P	K	W
O	M	A	L	A	R	S	A
E	Y	G	L	D	O	E	N
I	P	A	R	V	E	V	E

First find the theme, then fill in the names.

1. A – – M –
2. E – – – – – – – –
3. – – R –
4. – I – – – – – –
5. – – C – – – A –
6. N – – – –
7. P – – – – –
8. – – – – – R – – –
9. – E – – – – –
10. – – – – S
11. – I – – – –
12. – – – – – – – – D
13. – – – – E –
14. – – – N –
15. T – – – – –
16. – – S – – – – – –

An Abbreviated World History AD 1745 to 1899

(All in chronological order.)

THE B. OF P.P.

THE B.H. OF C.

C. OF Q. BY W.

S.J.I. BY J.H.

A.W. OF I.

G.W.B.F.P. OF U.S.

O. OF THE F.R.

B. OF THE N.

N.B.B.E. OF F.

I. OF R. BY N.

B. OF W.

THE C.W. *Civil War*

THE A.C.W.

P. OF Q.V. AS E. OF I.

T.I. BY A.G.B.

R.V. OF N.T.P.

B. OF THE B.W.

The Orchestra

Moving from square to square horizontally, vertically or diagonally find 24 words connected with an orchestra in the grid below. Squares may be used more than once but not in the same name. There are no redundant squares.

O	L	A	S	O	F	U	T	R	U
L	B	R	N	S	O	L	O	E	M
E	C	O	C	D	L	N	C	T	P
C	H	I	E	U	A	H	C	R	U
G	N	R	C	B	R	I	I	B	E
S	S	T	Y	M	W	P	A	S	L
I	O	U	C	P	O	A	N	M	L
N	M	R	E	D	O	L	G	U	B
O	B	G	T	I	W	I	E	R	G
N	E	A	N	D	V	N	D	E	L

flute
cello
violin
Trumpet

(a) *E PLURIBUS UNUM*

Fill in the blanks. The first letter of each spells out
another in the same theme.

1. – I – N – S – T –

2. – – – A – O – A

3. – E – R – S – –

4. – E – – E – – – E

5. – – – A – S – S

6. – E – – – E – – E – (2 words)

7. – – A – A – A

*(b) Fill in the words. The marked letters form an anagram
which explains the puzzle.

0.   ⌐ A – M

1.   – I – H – – I R (2 words)

2.   ⌐ – – G – T – R – E – E (2 words)

3.   – E – T ⌐ E – R – E – E (2 words)

4.   – O – E – A – E – R – E – E (2 words)

5.   ⌐ R – S – ⌐ R – E – E (2 words)

6.   – T – O – – – R – E – E (2 words)

7.   – O – E – A ⌐ E – A – E (2 words)

8.   – R – S – – A – E (2 words)

9.   – T – O – G – A – E (2 words)

10. – H – L – – A – E (2 words)

11. – T – R –

12. – ⌐ – R – C ⌐ N –

Three Cs

The following is a list of countries with their capitals and currency; however they have all been mixed up. Try to match them up again.

COUNTRY	CAPITAL	CURRENCY
Gambia	Male	Lek
Mongolia	Conakry	Colon
Guinea	Hamilton	Kip
Honduras	Doha	Franc
Costa Rica	Khartoum	Syli
Gabon	Tirana	Rupee
Laos	San Jose	Escudo
Paraguay	Ulan Bator	Pound
Albania	Vientiane	Riyal
Azores	Banjul	Guarani
Bermuda	Asuncion	Tughrik
Qatar	Tegucigalpa	Dollar
Maldive Islands	Libreville	Dalasi
Sudan	Ponta Delgada	Lampira

ODD ONE OUT

Remember, do not always look for the obvious—things are not always what they appear to be.

***(a)   Which is the odd one out?

   1. Chain
   2. Mail
   3. Plane
   4. Train
   5. Reign
   6. Rain

 *(b)   Which is the odd one out?

   1. Credit
   2. Energy
   3. Asleep
   4. Range
   5. Leased
   6. Greeny
   7. Tender
   8. Please
   9. Direct
   10. Anger
   11. Rented

Numbers

**(a)   Which of the following numbers is different to the rest?

    1. 743218

    2. 781138

    3. 786116

    4. 764124

    5. 781234

*(b)   Find the odd one out.

    7924,   4682,   3973,   3199,   2785

One of the following pairs does not belong with the others. Which is it?

1. Mike and Victor
2. Romeo and Juliet
3. Quebec and Lima
4. Rum and Brandy
5. Tango and Foxtrot

ANAGRAMS

There are a total of 41 anagrams which should satisfy the appetites of most anagram enthusiasts. The wheels have the added challenge of finding words from the anagram clues and the 'Enigmasig Wheels' are named after the Special Interest Group within Mensa mentioned in the introduction. Apart from the wheels, the anagrams are presented in a way which will become clear as you begin to solve them.

The Enigmasig Wheel (Mark I)

Complete the word in each column (all end in 'E'). Clues are anagrams in section to right of each column.

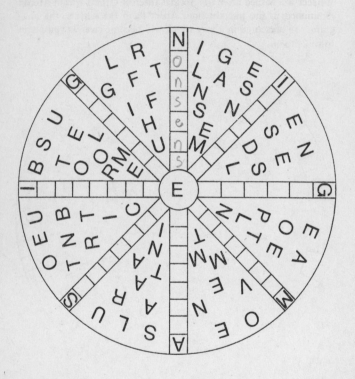

The Enigmasig Wheel (Mark II)

The anagrams in each section are a clue to both the word in the column to the left of each section (all end in 'E') and the word above the section (beginning and ending with the initial letters in the adjoining columns and reading clockwise).

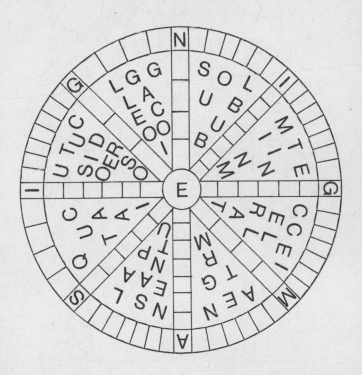

Solve the anagrams below. There are no two adjoining letters in the same circle/square/triangle.

*(a)

**(b)

**(c)

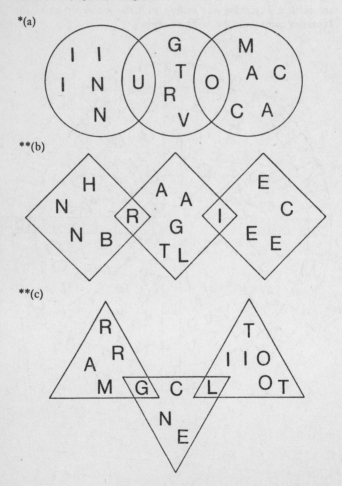

Solve the anagrams below. There are no two adjoining letters in the same shape.

**(a)

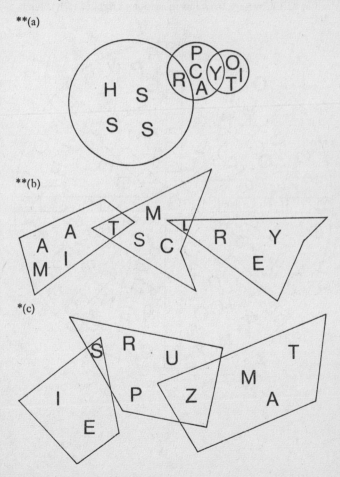

**(b)

*(c)

The Gallopers

The name given to this puzzle is the old fairground name for the roundabout ride on horses. Complete the words in each column (all end in 'G'). Clues are anagrams in section to right of each column.

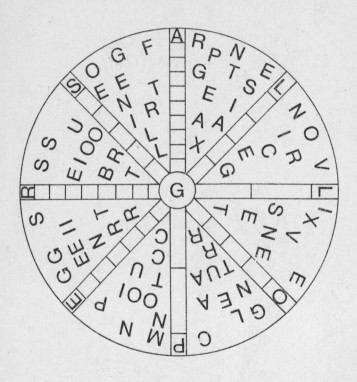

Solve the anagrams below. There are no two adjoining letters in the same shape.

**(a)

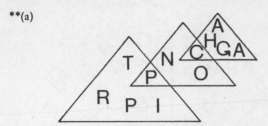

**(b)

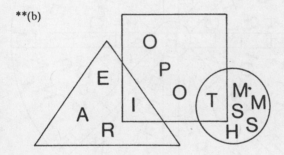

**(c)

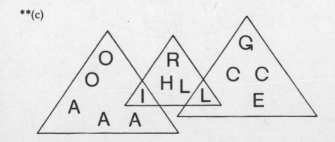

Complete the word in each column (all end in 'R'). Clues are anagrams in section to right of each column.

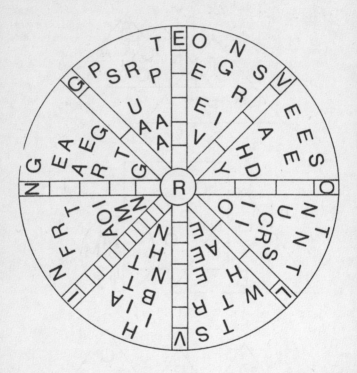

NUMBERS

Numbers can be interesting and challenging but often confusing, and it is fascinating how some numbers have their own individual characteristics. The puzzles are presented to give as varied a challenge as possible. You will solve some fairly quickly but others may need a fair amount of juggling with numbers. Please persevere as you will probably gain a great deal of satisfaction from sorting out a mass of digits to arrive finally at the correct answer.

Numbers can be fun, so calculators at the ready and good luck!

In each of the following place the digits into the grid so that each horizontal and vertical line can be divided by 11 reading either forwards or backwards.

**(a)   2, 2, 3, 3,
       4, 4, 4, 4,
       6, 6, 6,
       7, 7, 7, 7, 8

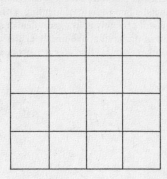

**(b)   1, 1, 1, 2, 2,
       3, 3, 3, 3,
       4, 4, 6,
       8, 9, 9, 9

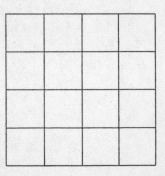

(If you find yourself struggling you may find it helpful to refer to puzzle 96 (a).)

Find the Calculation

***(a)   Using the figure 5 eight times together with any mathematical symbols, with the exception of plus signs, write out a calculation to give the answer 110. Find two answers.

**(b)   Using the figure 6 seven times, together with any mathematical symbols, write out a calculation to give the answer 5832.

*(c)   Using the figure 7 seven times, together with any mathematical symbols, write out a calculation to give the answer 7777.

Place all the digits below in the grid so that all the numbers when read both forwards and backwards are divisible by 37. Lines reading downwards contain the following numbers:

(A) 1,1,1,1,1,3

(B) 2, 3, 4, 4, 5, 5, 6, 8, 9

(C) 3, 3, 5, 7, 8, 9

(D) 1, 1, 2, 2, 2, 7, 8, 8, 8

(E) 1, 5

(F) 1, 2, 2, 7, 7, 8

(G) 1, 1, 6, 7, 7, 7

(H) 4, 5, 6, 6, 7, 8

(I) 2, 2, 2, 3, 3, 3, 5, 6, 7, 9

(J) 2, 2, 5, 5, 6, 9

(K) 0, 2, 2, 3, 3, 6, 6, 7

(L) 2, 2, 2, 4, 4, 6

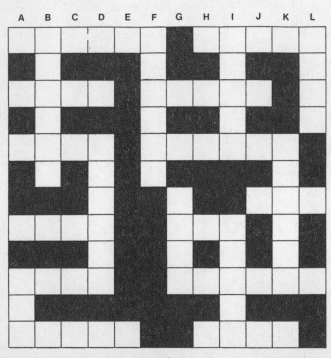

The Golf Club Statistician

I won all three major knockout competitions at my Golf Club last year (wishful thinking) even though I was the only player unlucky enough to be drawn in both preliminary rounds.

Recently our club statistician stopped me and said, 'Do you know, I cubed the number of entrants for each competition and the last digit of each of the three resultant numbers is the same as your golf handicap and the sum of the three middle digits, i.e. the middle digit of each of the three cube numbers, is the same as mine; also the total number of rounds you won is the same as your wife's handicap which is exactly double your own handicap; furthermore the total number of matches played, including the end of season consolation event for players knocked out in the preliminary rounds, is the same as the age of Seth Arkwright, our oldest surviving founder member?'

What are mine, my wife's and the club statistician's handicaps and how old is Seth Arkwright?

The Magic Number Nine

Place the digits below into the grid in such a way that all the horizontal and vertical lines when read both forwards and backwards will divide exactly by 9. It will assist you in knowing that the sum of the digits of each line will also divide by nine.

1, 1, 1, 2, 2, 2, 2, 2, 3, 3, 4, 4, 4, 5, 5, 6, 7, 7, 7, 7, 8, 8, 8, 9, 9.

In each of the following find the missing numbers:

*(a) 2, 3, 4, 6, 8, 12, ?, ?, 32, 48, 96.

*(b) 1, 5, 14, 30, 55, ?, 140.

*(c) 2, 3, 4, 6, 9, 12, ?, 36.

Place the digits in the track in such a way that the sum of any three consecutive digits round the track can be divided by three.

1, 1, 1, 1, 2, 2, 2, 3, 3, 3, 3, 4, 4, 5, 5, 5, 5, 5, 6, 6, 6, 6, 6, 7, 7, 7, 7, 8, 8, 9, 9, 9.

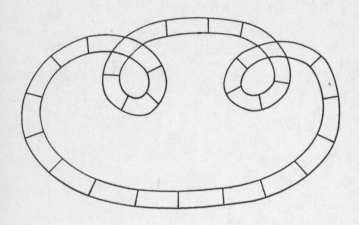

The Door Number Puzzle

Two workmen were putting the finishing touches to a new door they had fitted to house number 3861. All that was left to do was screw the metal digits to the door.

(a) Being a Mensan, Phil could not resist challenging Ken by asking him if he could screw the digits onto the door to give a four figure number which could not be divided exactly by 9.

(b) When they had sorted that out Ken then asked Phil if he could screw the same digits onto the door to give a four figure number which could not be divided exactly by 3.

What is the answer to both problems? Can either of them be done?

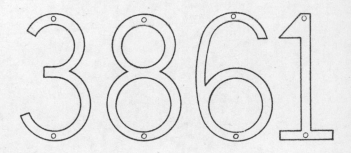

39
Find the Calculation

*(a) Fill in the digits from 1 to 9 to complete the addition sum.

```
  * * *
  * * *
  * * *
─────────
1 9 0 8
```

***(b) By using the digits 0–9 once each only (excluding the answer) devise an addition sum to give the answer 52.2.

Cubes and Squares

This puzzle almost made the Brainbender section. If you haven't a calculator I hope you have plenty of fingers and toes.

ACROSS	DOWN
A. CUBE	A. CUBE
E. SQUARE	B. CUBE
G. CUBE	C. SQUARE
H. SQUARE	D. CUBE
I. SQUARE	E. CUBE
L. SQUARE	F. CUBE/SQUARE
M. CUBE	J. CUBE
P. CUBE	K. CUBE
Q. CUBE	L. SQUARE
R. SQUARE	N. SQUARE
	O. SQUARE

CATEGORISE

The word puzzles in this chapter are the second of the general knowledge sections in the book. Dividing the groups into threes will not prove as easy as it appears at first glance but this should make it all the more interesting.

Arrange into groups of three

Abode
Bar
Bicycle
Home
Lever
Macmillan
Pedal
Residence
Rod
Roof
Straw
Thatcher

Arrange into groups of three

Argon
Chamois
Corsica
Crete
Cyprus
Eland
Elba
Gallium
Sardinia
St Helena
Xenon
Zebu

Arrange into groups of three

121
148
157
162
174
246
277
389
437
575
633
681

Ashdod
Creation
Elijah
Haydn
Hebrides
Israel
Jaffa
Mendelssohn
Minch
Seasons
Stornoway
Western Isles

*45
Arrange into groups of three

Brobdingnag
Excursion
Expedition
Fast
Journey
Lilliput
Migration
Quick
Rapid
Swallow
Swift
Travels

***46
Arrange into groups of three

Agamemnon
Congo
Copenhagen
Elias
Helsinki
Kamet
Kenya
Niger
Nile
Obi
Oslo
Stockholm

Not everyone will be familiar with the word 'rebus', however, most people will recall books at school where the words were represented by pictures and symbols. Well these are rebuses.

To give a couple of examples:

might represent 'TEA-TIME' and

   o

   o

AYE o

   o

   o

might represent 'HAWAII 50'

You really will need to use your imagination to solve the rebuses that follow and then you will probably wish to have a go at inventing some of your own.

```
            T
        T       T
      T   T   T   T
    T   T       T   T
```

```
          N N
        N       N
      N           N
    N               N
    N               N
      N           N
        N       N
          N N
```

```
    I I I I I I I I I I
    S S S S S S S S S S
```

```
::
::
::
::::::
```

***52
Solve the Rebus
```
           l
      i i i
i i i
```
Solve the Rebus

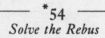

DES
DES

YAW

N
W
O
D

QUOTATIONS

Eight quotations are to be found in this section in a variety of disguises. Great enjoyment can be obtained from reading quotations and it is often surprising to find who originated, hundreds, sometimes thousands, of years ago, phrases we still use frequently today in our every day speech. The following, for example, were all written by the same man:

'The world's mine oyster'
'The better part of valour is discretion'
'Be to yourself as you would to your friend'
'If money go before all ways do lie open'
'All that glisters is not gold'
'Ill blows the wind that profits nobody'

An anagram of his name is, very aptly, 'I'll make a wise phrase' (answer on p. 120).

Two in One

In each of the following, two quotations are squashed together. All the letters are in the correct order. Find the two quotations. To assist, the writers' names follow the quotations but have been put together in the same way.

**(a) FALORLTGHEINTFORGSGCIOVMEETCOOHNIC
MLUWHDOWEAINLDLBBUEAGTWRAIETED.
— SLOHNGAFKELESLPOEAWRE

**(b) TAHEBSONENLCEYMWAAYKETSTOHEHHAEAV
REATFGRRIOEWNFDONISDTEOBREONE.
— EMBEARYSLOYN

Starting at the top left-hand corner, work horizontally, vertically and diagonally to find some useful philosophy. Nine letters are redundant which form an anagram of the philosopher who wrote this (a long time ago).

START

T	S	P	N	T	E	D	U
I	H	I	H	N	T	E	S
E	E	W	E	T	U	H	P
T	R	R	O	R	E	A	P
O	S	R	O	B	A	H	Y
C	F	F	E	E	R	C	E
H	T	S	C	S	O	H	G
I	A	N	E	F	A	N	I

In each of the following find the starting point, fill in the blanks and a quotation will appear. The missing letters form an anagram of the writer.

*(a)

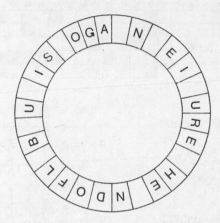

**(b)

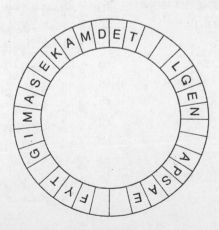

*60
Acrostic

Solve the clues, place each letter in its appropriate position in the grid and a quotation will appear.

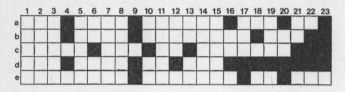

	1	2	3	4	5	6	7	8	9	10	11	12	13	14	15	16	17	18	19	20	21	22	23
a																							
b																							
c																							
d																							
e																							

Clue		Answer cells
EMOTIONAL TREMOR	(6)	16c 2c 20b 11e 7a 14a
CROOKED	(4)	17b 15b 6e 17a
SUBJECT OF ESSAY	(5)	1c 18a 8b 10e 16b
IN SUCH MANNER	(2)	11d 3c
RENOWN	(4)	19e 19b 5b 15a
SCIENCE OF REALITY	(8)	5a 6a 13d 22a 9d 20c 8c 8a
MENTAL PENETRATION	(7)	10d 1b 12e 18c 1e 2a 8e
THROW ABOUT	(4)	5e 2b 4c 12b
BARBAROUS	(7)	6d 3a 7d 1a 14d 5c 2d
BACKLESS SEAT	(7)	18e 8d 5d 12c 10b 1d 19c
MILITARY UNIFORM	(5)	7b 17c 21e 15e 11b
RIGHT OF ACCESS	(6)	21b 14c 13e 2e 16e 11a
POSSESSED	(3)	8c 14b 3d
MODIFY	(5)	4e 21a 14e 10a 13b
FUSS	(3)	6b 11c 12a
COLLECTIVE STAKES	(4)	13a 15c 19a 22e
TUNEFUL	(5)	7e 7c 15d 3e 3b

BRAINBENDERS

This section is named 'Brainbenders' simply because I believe the puzzles to be some of the most difficult in the book. If I had to choose the most difficult of them all it would be the cross-alphabet (64), but remember every puzzle has a solution and can be solved, eventually.

Treasure Chest

The explorer goes through the maze to the treasure chest by moving from letter to letter, vertically, horizontally or diagonally to discover the hidden message. There are seven redundant letters which are an anagram of the contents of the treasure chest.

ENTER

Y	W	A	F	O	O	N	O
U	O	E	R	F	R	C	N
R	R	D	S	E	T	D	G
F	S	G	I	A	N	R	T
R	O	H	R	E	A	U	A
T	T	S	T	S	N	A	L
A	F	I	A	O	T	I	O
N	C	T	I	H	I	N	S

TREASURE CHEST

Squares

Complete the grid below to give square numbers only using the following digits (2 already filled in):

1, 1, 1, 1, 1, 2, 2, 2, 2, 2, 2, 2, 2, (3), 4, 4, 4, 4, 4, 4, 5, 5, 5, 5, (6), 6, 6, 6, 6, 6, 6, 7, 8, 8, 8, 8, 9, 9, 9, 9, 9, 0.

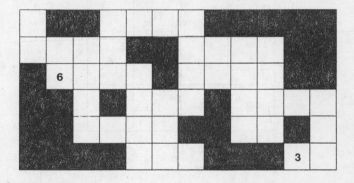

A Magic Word Square

Fill in the missing letters.

D	I	G	I
I	O	N	
	I		A
S	E	R	P

This is the first of three cross alphabet puzzles I have included in this book. This one is included in the Brainbender section because it is the most difficult. Some months ago a similar puzzle appeared in the *Mensa Journal* and was solved by only one person, so if you are successful you know just how well you have done. The object is to put each of the 26 letters of the alphabet into the grid once only to form a crossword. There are no clues; what is required is a great deal of juggling with letters and words.

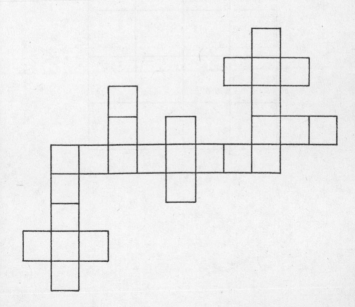

A Magic Number Square

Fill the grid below with the numbers 1–16 to form a magic square so that each vertical and horizontal line, each corner to corner diagonal line, the four corner numbers, each block of four corner squares and the middle four block of numbers each add up to 34. Number 7 filled in for good luck.

7			

Ego Booster

Commence at the top left-hand corner and travel to the bottom right-hand corner by moving from letter to letter, vertically, horizontally or diagonally to unscramble the hidden message. Visit each square once only. There are no redundant letters.

START

W	E	S	I	H	B	E	Y	D	D
C	H	S	F	S	T	D	O	N	O
C	U	E	P	U	E	E	T	B	U
S	N	L	L	U	V	T	I	Q	A
U	Y	Y	Z	O	E	T	I	L	U
C	O	Z	R	L	S	E	N	A	N
Y	O	L	P	P	O	I	O	P	D
O	E	M	E	F	A	T	A	T	I
W	U	L	V	D	N	I	R	N	E
I	L	H	A	E	T	E	M	C	E

FINISH

MISSING LINKS

This is very similar to the first section in that you are required to identify relationships between numbers, words and diagrammatic representation. You will need to open your mind to every possibility, be prepared for the unexpected and not take everything at face value. Then you will start coming up with the right answers.

Fill in the Missing Numbers

74862	2688	

82687		630

79988		

Fill in the Missing Numbers

15707	3.1.44	

	6·10·47	19444

26632		

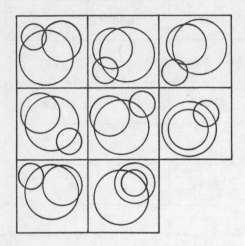

Choose from:

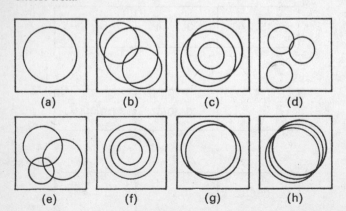

(a) (b) (c) (d)

(e) (f) (g) (h)

Fill in the Missing Numbers

1248		4096

428		

4812	8	

Fill in the Missing Letters
then Find the Missing Square

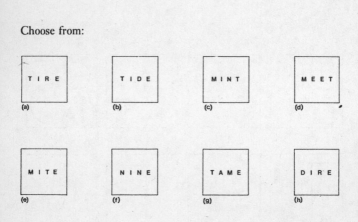

E – I –	– M – –	T – – –
T – – –	R – – E	– M I –
D – – –	– I – –	?

Choose from:

TIRE (a)	TIDE (b)	MINT (c)	MEET (d)
MITE (e)	NINE (f)	TAME (g)	DIRE (h)

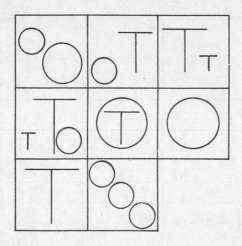

Choose from:

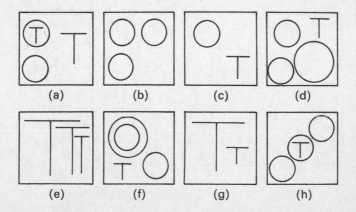

Fill in the Missing Numbers
then Find the Missing Square

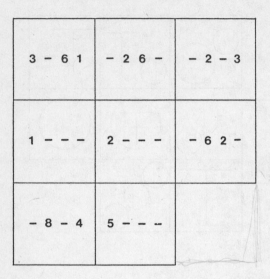

Choose from:

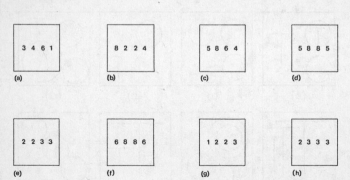

| 3 | | 6 | 30 |

| 9 | 15 | 20 | 180 |

| 8 | 9 | 15 | 16 | 20 | |

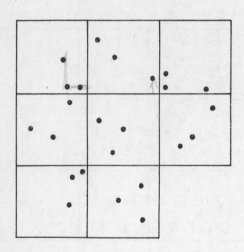

Choose from:

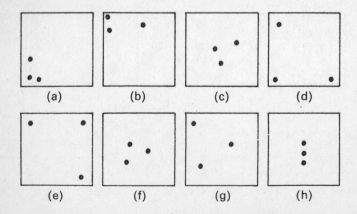

TEASERS

A selection of eight teasers. You will probably spot the answers to some fairly quickly but others just may trick you and it will be those that you will wish to try out on your friends.

Tiddlywinks Championship

There was a total of 229 matches played in our local open amateur knockout Tiddlywinks Championships last year. One player scratched out of the preliminary round because of illness and another from the third round because of holidays. Without doing any written calculation can you say how many players entered the competition?

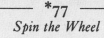
If a wheel is spun containing an equal number of black and white segments, what are the chances of each of the following combinations appearing against an arrow above the top of the wheel in any two consecutive spins?

      (a)   White—white
      (b)   White—black

When I was a schoolboy I composed and memorised the following. For what purpose?

'Now I know a super utterance to assist maths.'

On the evening before the night when the clocks were put back an hour to mark the end of Summer Time Mr Riddle phoned his solicitor to make an appointment for the following morning. When the solicitor asked the time of the appointment Mr Riddle said '11 hours after it takes the Town Hall clock 10 seconds to strike the hour.' 'Doesn't the Town Hall clock strike at 1-second intervals?', asked the solicitor. 'Yes,' said Mr Riddle. 'OK, then, that's easy enough to work out,' said the solicitor. What was the time of the appointment?

*80
Colours

How many colours are necessary to fill in the grid below so that no two sections containing the same colours have adjoining boundaries.

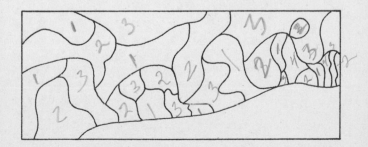

Cardboard Boxes

A cardboard box manufacturer was considering doubling the volume of his square boxes. On hearing of this his supplier of cardboard decided to encourage him to place the extra business by offering a very generous 37.5 per cent quantity discount on his new total turnover figure. How much extra would the box manufacturer have to pay for the additional cardboard if he decided to go ahead?

Wooden Cubes

By using two wooden cubes placed side by side and by numbering each side of each cube with one digit only, what is the highest number which can be displayed by starting at 1 then working upwards and not omitting any subsequent numbers?

Both cubes must be used for each number but they can be switched round.

The Generous Duke

The kindly Duke decided to give three of his servants a piece of land each as a long service award. He gave each a length of wire 144 yards long and some posts and instructed the first to mark out his land in the form of an equilateral triangle, the second in the form of a circle and the third in the form of a square. Which, if any, received the greatest area of land and which received least?

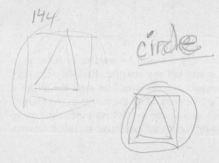

WORDS

60 words to be found in various disguises. The type of puzzle, like anagrams, that looks easy once you know the answer. Personally, I find the Cross-Alphabet puzzles fascinating to compile and always try to achieve as compact a version as possible. I would be interested to learn which is the most compact X-Alpha puzzle possible in the English language. The ultimate 'impossible' version would be to insert the 26 letters of the alphabet into the grid below so that each horizontal and vertical line forms a word.

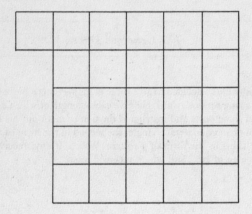

I very much doubt, however, if it would be possible to get near to this as only five vowels would kill any attempt. Probably the only way to find the most compact version would be with the aid of a computer and a data base consisting of all the words in the Oxford English Dictionary which do not use any letters more than once, however, I will very gladly leave that challenge to the computer buffs.

Find the Words

Fill in the spaces to find the words. All letters are in the correct order and the overlapping letter appears twice.

**(a)   16-letter word.

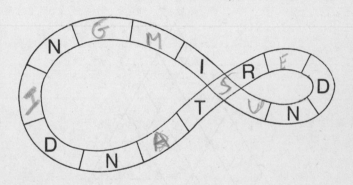

**(b)   13-letter word.

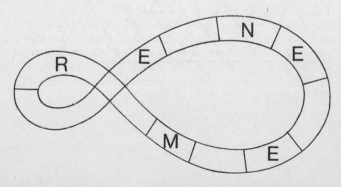

Using the following letters only, fill in the pyramid so that each horizontal line forms a word. Use each letter as many times as necessary. Each word formed must consist of same letters as word above it, in any order, plus one additional letter. (9-letter base.)

C, E, I, N, O, P, R, T

94

Cross-Alphabet

Place each of the 26 letters of the alphabet into the grid once only to form a crossword.

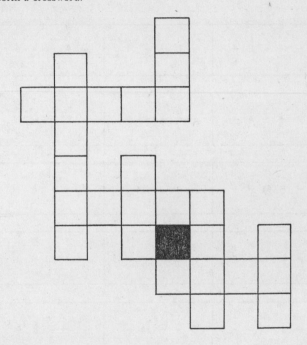

CLUES (in no particular order)

Animal
Fluent
Hit high
Nervous
Immoral practice
Stone of pure crystalline silica
Strap
Beaded moisture

Fill in the spaces to find the missing words. There is only one correct answer.

- - - E -	- L - - T	- A - - R

S - - A -	- - - P -	- L E - -

- - M - -	- I - R -	T - - E -

- - I - E	- M - - -	- - L - S

- I L - -	S - - N -	- - - K -

- E S - -	- T - E -	- R - - -

Using the following letters only, fill in the pyramid so each horizontal line forms a word. Use each letter as many times as necessary. Each word formed must consist of same letters as word above it, in any order, plus one additional letter. (10–letter base.)

A,   B,   D,   E,   I,   L,   R,   T

Fill in the missing letters and find the nine-letter words.

* (a)

A	T	
T	E	A
I		L

*** (b)

N	A	
	R	E
I	P	

* (c)

	L	O
S	E	
I		K

** (d)

M		O
E		R
	R	A

** (e)

E		C
	N	U
I	S	

Place each of the 26 letters of the alphabet into the grid once only to form a crossword.

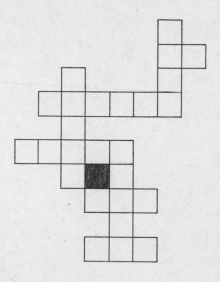

CLUES (in no particular order)

Across

Liquid measurement
Distress
Denoting ownership
Legendary maidens
Child

Down

Numerical indication
'H'-shaped
Pieces of work

CODES

Codes aren't everyone's cup of tea but they can be interesting in moderation. There is a fun code to start with and then they become progressively more difficult.

Ale Inn Cann's Code

A famous American, during the Civil War, used his own very special code when sending messages. He used the signature "ALE INN CANN" instead of his usual signature which was, of course, A. Lincoln. The sound was exactly the same but the words were different. If that's clear then try decoding the following cryptograms based on the same code which could have been sent by certain famous historical characters.

(a) K. wee Nell is a bath spa knees are madder deaf it head barque Sue Noon wit trees or France est Dr. Ache.

(b) Mr K. Ant any mill K. Mandy live red plea said rope bite on hight hand screw rub M. high B. hack K. Lee hope hat, Hoorah!

**(a) C18V2C99 C3V4C11V2!
C10V2C1515V1C5V2
C15V5C22V2C15154V5C9920
C3V2C2V4C3V2C3

***(b) 72 11212 785 381313125 62129556 1082
8195 3556595554 3179517121 2 (?), 72
453245 7896 13566175, 3217517812179216!

Decode the Following

XCNAWQ XU AHIWXAON HUJKGI GIXXIC EUCHL
MWH ZUYYUW IWHAWQL LJZR ML 'IC' MWH 'AWQ'
ZMW KI UO ZUWLAHICMKGI MLLALXMWZI ERIW
MXXIYFXAWQ XU HIZUHI YILLMQIL UO XRAL XNFI.
MHHAXAUWMG AWOUCYMXAUW, OUC ISMYFGI,
TWUEAWQ XRMX XRI GIXXIC 'I' AL XRI YULX
ZUYYUW GIXXIC AW XRI IWQGALR GMWQJMQI MWH
XRMX 'AWQ' AL XRI YULX ZUYYUW XRCII GIXXIC
EUCH IWHAWQ AL MGLU EUCXR TWUEAWQ.

AD FINUM

Ken Russell, the Puzzle Editor of *British Mensa Journal*, always includes a 'Kick-Self' puzzle in his monthly column. Several of the puzzles included in this chapter are in the same spirit and if you don't solve them you may wish to kick yourself once you know the answer.

Find the missing squares.

**(a)

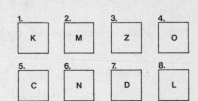

*(b)

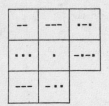

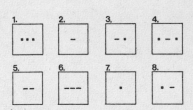

*(a)   The following car licence plate is incomplete:

ROY   GB   I

To complete the plate choose one of the following:

T, U, V, W, X, Y, Z

**(b)   Find the next to complete the sequence.

C, A, J, A, C, ?

Choose from:

A, C, L, J, P, V.

***(a) Without using either multiplication or division find out *quickly* which of the following numbers can be divided exactly by eleven:

(1) 504856

(2) 358938

(3) 8679

(4) 920986

(5) 3105

*(b) Find two 15-letter words which apart from the initial letter are spelt exactly the same.

*(c) Show how $14^2 - 3^2 = 187$, without actually squaring either the 14 or the 3.

Remember Phil and Ken? They are now fitting a door to house number 73413. Ken threw out the challenge this time and asked Phil if he could screw all the digits to the door to display a number which could not be divided by 3. Could it be done?

Find the missing square.

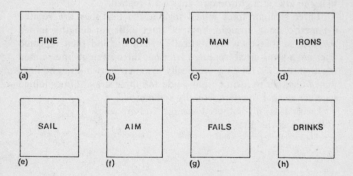

PAPER	INK	COIN
KNEE	SUN	ARM
IRON	LINK	

Choose from:

FINE	MOON	MAN	IRONS
(a)	(b)	(c)	(d)
SAIL	AIM	FAILS	DRINKS
(e)	(f)	(g)	(h)

There's no doubt it sure is a zzz,
Hit it now or give it a pass,
 Soon xxxxx to its charms,
 Never tire pulling arms,
Dare you give it a spin; xzzxxzxx?

My wife asked me what I was buying her for her birthday. Never liking to give straightforward answers I replied:

'Three straight lines joined together so that they are rotated symmetric, four straight lines of three different lengths joined together so that they are vertically symmetric and then repeated later on, a semi-circle repeated later on, three straight lines joined together so that they are vertically symmetric, two straight lines joined together to form a right-angle and three straight lines joined together so that they are laterally symmetric.'

'I wish I hadn't bothered asking,' said my wife.

What was the gift?

ANSWERS

I hope you found the puzzles enjoyable and that you were able to come up with many of the answers. For the puzzles which you were unable to crack, you should find that the explanations provided will give you a clear idea of what you should have done to come up with the correct solution. Good luck and keep puzzling!

Should you be interested in learning more about Mensa and how to take the Mensa Entrance Tests, and find out your own 'IQ' level, write to:

British Mensa Ltd., American Mensa Ltd., Australian Mensa,
Bond House, 2626 E 14 Street, 16 Elliot Avenue,
St. John's Square, Brooklyn, Carnegie,
Wolverhampton, N.Y. 11235. Victoria 3163.
WV2 4AH.

1. Proceed via $3-3^2-3^3-3^4$, i.e. $3-9-27-81-243$ etc.

2. (b)—to complete every possible pairing of the four symbols.

3. (a) 256—it is the square of the sum of the digits of the preceding number, i.e. $(1+6+9)^2$.

   (b) 26496—a complex but logical sequence which progresses as follows: 126 $(12 \times 6) = 72 \times (1+2+6) = 648$ $(64 \times 8) = 512 \times (6+4+8) = 9216$ $(92 \times 16) = 1472 \times (9+2+1+6) = 26496$.

   (c) 96—rearrange the digits 864 in every possible way, then divide each resulting number by 9.

4. Proceed via prime numbers, i.e. $2-3-5-7-11-13-17$ up to 43.

5. (a) T—i.e. Two-Four-Six etc.

   (b) T—i.e. laterally symmetric.

   (c) P—i.e. no symmetries.

6. (a) HOOD—each word can be prefixed by the word MAN to form another word.

(b) KNOT—all the words have their letters in alphabetical order.

(c) CAUTIONED—all the words contain all five vowels.

7. (d)—when two symbols touch, they disappear from the next square and two new symbols are introduced. The remaining two symbols retain their position.

8. (c)—to solve this puzzle it is first necessary to realise that the arms attached to the central vertical line move round clockwise in the next drawing. This rules out option (b). Secondly, as the top circle and bottom square never change, option (f) can be discounted. The third, and most complex, part of the puzzle is working out the sequence of the symbols to the left and right of the main horizontal line. In the second drawing the left and right symbols from the first drawing have merged at the left-hand side and a new symbol has been introduced on the right. In the third drawing the symbols which merged have now moved out of the drawing, the cross has moved over to the left and a new figure, a circle, has been introduced. The sequence is then repeated, i.e. in the fourth drawing the cross and circle have merged on the left and the new symbol (—) is introduced. The answer, therefore, is (c) where the cross/circle combination has disappeared, symbol (—) has moved over to the left and a completely new symbol (.) has been introduced.

9. (a) QUARTER—it is the next highest measure of capacity.

(b) DUBLIN—it is part of a State or County (represented by *Texas*). Texas is part of a Country (represented by *France*). France is part of a Continent (represented by *Asia*). Asia is part of a Planet (represented by *Neptune*). Neptune orbits a Star (represented by *Sirius*).

(c) TUBA (ABUT)—all the words form another word when read backwards.

(d) MAD—each word can be prefixed by the word NO to form another word.

10. (a)—the secret of this puzzle is that there are three different elements in each circle which move in a different but logical sequence on a white background, numbered 1–8. The striped element simply moves one position anti-clockwise, then back again clockwise. The black element moves one position clockwise, then two clockwise, then three clockwise, and continues increasing its number of movements by one each time. The most complex movement is of the dotted element. This first moves one position anti-clockwise, then two positions anti-clockwise, but then changes direction and moves back one position clockwise, then two positions clockwise, then changes direction again and continues in this manner.

11. RACHMANINOV, GOUNOD, SCHUMANN, BEETHOVEN, ELGAR, BIZET, TSCHAIKOVSKY, MASCAGNI, SCHUBERT, MENDELSSOHN, MEYERBEER, BERLIOZ, PUCCINI, STRAVINSKY, WAGNER. ANAGRAM: ENIGMA VARIATIONS.

12. TROJAN WAR, DEATH OF ALEXANDER THE GREAT AT BABYLON, ROMAN INVASION OF BRITAIN, REVOLT OF BOADICEA, DARK AGES, NORMAN CONQUEST OF ENGLAND, MAGNA CARTA SEALED BY KING JOHN, MODEL PARLIAMENT, HUNDRED YEARS WAR, REBELLION OF WAT TYLER, BATTLE OF AGINCOURT, JOAN OF ARC BURNED AT ROUEN, WARS OF ROSES ENDED BY BATTLE OF BOSWORTH, CHRISOPHER COLUMBUS DISCOVERED AMERICA, SIR FRANCIS DRAKE SAILED ROUND WORLD, GUNPOWDER PLOT, CIVIL WAR IN ENGLAND, OLIVER CROMWELL BECAME LORD PROTECTOR, GREAT FIRE OF LONDON, ACCESSION OF PETER THE GREAT OF RUSSIA, UNION OF ENGLAND AND SCOTLAND, SOUTH SEA BUBBLE.

13. ANTIGUA, MARTINIQUE, SEYCHELLES, SUDAN, UGANDA, YEMEN, DUBAI, ALGERIA, ANGOLA, INDONESIA, SENEGAL, COLOMBIA, RWANDA. ANAGRAM: DAMASCUS, SYRIA.

14. FINE DRIZZLE, DRY SHERRY, AWFULLY GOOD, SLIPPED UP, SWEET SORROW, GOOD GRIEF, STAND DOWN, STANDING JUMP, RETIRED PERMANENT SECRETARY, FUTURE HISTORY, SIT UP, WAR GAMES, SPEND THRIFT, PERFECTLY AWFUL, ADVANCE TO THE REAR, ADVANCED BEGINNERS, FEELING NUMB, BITTER SWEET, LOOSE FIT, HOT CHILLI, BAD GOODS.

15. JAY, MAGPIE, CORMORANT, CUCKOO, ROBIN, ORIOLE, MALLARD, LINNET, LAPWING, WREN, PARTRIDGE, REDWING, LARK, SPARROW, DOVE, REEVE, SWAN, PARROT, ROOK, ROC, LANNER, TERCEL, KA, SORA, GANNET, GOWK, LOON, RAIL, REEDLING, RINGTAIL, SERIN, COB.

16. 'AMERICAN PRESIDENTS' SPELT OUT IN QUESTION: ADAMS, EISENHOWER, FORD, FILLMORE, BUCHANAN, NIXON, PIERCE, JEFFERSON, KENNEDY, HAYES, WILSON, CLEVELAND, HOOVER, GRANT, TRUMAN, WASHINGTON.

17. BATTLE OF PRESTON PANS, BLACK HOLE OF CALCUTTA, CAPTURE OF QUEBEC BY WOLFE, SPINNING JENNY INVENTED BY JAMES HARGREAVES, AMERICAN WAR OF INDEPENDENCE, GEORGE WASHINGTON BECOMES FIRST PRESIDENT OF UNITED STATES, OUTBREAK OF FRENCH REVOLUTION, BATTLE OF NILE, NAPOLEON BONAPARTE BECOMES EMPEROR OF FRANCE, INVASION OF RUSSIA BY NAPOLEON, BATTLE OF WATERLOO, THE CRIMEAN WAR, THE AMERICAN CIVIL WAR, PROCLAMATION OF QUEEN VICTORIA AS EMPRESS OF INDIA, TELEPHONE INVENTED BY ALEXANDER GRAHAM BELL, REVISED VERSION OF NEW TESTAMENT PUBLISHED, BEGINNING OF THE BOER WAR.

18. CONDUCTOR, CONCERTO, HORNS, CYMBALS, OBOE, BASSOON, STRINGS, CELLO, HARP,

PICCOLO, BRASS, PERCUSSION, TROMBONE,
ORGAN, FLUTE, TRUMPET, WOODWIND, VIOLA,
VIOLIN, TRIANGLE, TUBA, BELLS, DRUMS,
BUGLE.

19. (a) 1. *M*INNESOTA
2. *O*KLAHOMA
3. *N*EBRASKA
4. *T*ENNESSEE
5. *A*RKANSAS
6. *N*EW JERSEY
7. *A*LABAMA

'E PLURIBUS UNUM' means 'one out of many' and is
the motto of the United States of America.

(b) 0. CALM
1. LIGHT AIR
2. SLIGHT BREEZE
3. GENTLE BREEZE
4. MODERATE BREEZE
5. FRESH BREEZE
6. STRONG BREEZE
7. MODERATE GALE
8. FRESH GALE
9. STRONG GALE
10. WHOLE GALE
11. STORM
12. HURRICANE

ANAGRAM—BEAUFORT SCALE.

20. ALBANIA, TIRANA, LEK; AZORES, PONTA
DELGADA, ESCUDO; BERMUDA, HAMILTON,
DOLLAR; COSTA RICA, SAN JOSE, COLON;
GABON, LIBREVILLE, FRANC; GAMBIA, BANJUL,
DALASI; GUINEA, CONAKRY, SYLI; HONDURAS,
TEGUCIGALPA, LAMPIRA; LAOS, VIENTIANE,
KIP; MALDIVE ISLANDS, MALE, RUPEE;
MONGOLIA, ULAN BATOR, TUGHRIK;
PARAGUAY, ASUNCION, GUARANI; QATAR,
DOHA, RIYAL; SUDAN, KHARTOUM, POUND.

21. (a) TRAIN (others are anagrams of countries).

(b) LEASED (others pair, i.e. DIRECT/CREDIT using the same letters).

22. (a) 3—product of digits differs.

(b) 4682—sum digits differs.

23. 4—the others are part of the International Phonetic Alphabet.

24. NONSENSE (MEANINGLESS), INFINITE (ENDLESS), GAZELLE (ANTELOPE), MANOEUVRE (MOVEMENT), ABORIGINE (AUSTRALIAN), SUBSCRIBE (CONTRIBUTE), IRRITABLE (TROUBLESOME), GRUESOME (FRIGHTFUL).

25. NARCISSI, NERINE (BULBOUS), IMMEDIATE, IMPENDING (IMMINENT), GALVANISM, GENERATE (ELECTRICAL), MANTLE, MANTILLA (GARMENT), ATROCIOUS, ABOMINATE (UNPLEASANT), SCAMPI, SARDINE (AQUATIC), IMPOLITE, INSULTING (DISCOURTEOUS), GORGE, GRABEN (GEOLOGICAL).

26. (a) CIRCUMNAVIGATION.

(b) INTERCHANGEABLE.

(c) TRIGONOMETRICAL.

27. (a) ASTROPHYSICS.

(b) ASYMMETRICAL.

(c) TRAPEZIUMS.

28. AGGRAVATING (EXASPERATING), LINING (COVERING), LONG (EXTENSIVE), OBLONG (RECTANGULAR), PANG (COMPUNCTION), ENTERING (REGISTERING), ROLLICKING (BOISTEROUS), SCRYING (FORETELLING).

29. (a) PANTOGRAPHIC.

(b) METAMORPHOSIS.

(c) ARCHAEOLOGICAL.

30. EMPEROR (SOVEREIGN), VISOR (EYESHADE),
ORDER (INSTRUCTION), LOVER (SWEETHEART),
VILLAGER (INHABITANT), INTELLIGENCER
(INFORMANT), NUMBER (AGGREGATE), GEAR
(APPARATUS).

31. (a) 6842
3762
4367
7447

(b) 2981
3124
4136
3993

32. (a) $5.5 - 5 \times 55 \times (5 - \frac{5}{5})$ *or* $\frac{555}{5} - \frac{55}{55}$

(b) $\dfrac{6^6}{\frac{6}{6} + \frac{6}{6} + 6}$

(c) $\dfrac{7777 \times 7}{\sqrt{7 \times 7}}$

33. Lines Down:

(A) 1131111   (G) 171776

(B) 443556892   (H) 566784

(C) 735893   (I) 3352273926

(D) 822117882   (J) 552296

(E) 51   (K) 03326672

(F) 221778   (L) 244226

34. To solve this puzzle it is essential to pick up the opening
clue that there were only *two* preliminary rounds, therefore,
the number of entries for *one* of the competitions must have
been either 4, 8, 16, 32, 64 etc. so that no preliminary
rounds were necessary. From there by some trial and error
it is possible to arrive at the following solution, which is the
only one which meets the requirements of the remainder of
the puzzle:

Entries	(Cube)	Players in 1st Round	Players in Preliminaries	Preliminary round losers	Matches	My rounds
22	(10648)	10	12	6	21	5
32	(32768)	32	0	0	31	5
42	(74088)	22	20	10	41	6
—						
13						

CONSOLATION EVENT

16		16	0		15	
					108	16

My handicap = 8.   My wife's handicap = 16.
Club Statistician's handicap = 13.   Seth Arkwright's age
= 108.

35. 47637
     22212
     83457
     91782
     45819

36. (a) 16, 24—they are the factors of the final number 96.

(b) 91—start at 0 and add progressive square numbers, i.e.
$0+1=1$, $1+4=5$, $5+9=14$, $14+16=30$,
$30+25=55$, $55+36=91$, $91+49=140$.

(c) 18—they are the factors of the final number 36.

37. Starting immediately to the right of the right hand
overlapping number and moving clockwise, insert the digits
in the grid as follows:

5, 3, 7, 5, 9, 1, 8, 9, 4, 2, 6, 7, 2, 3, 7, 8 (left-hand
overlapping number), 3, 1, 5, 6, 4 (8 already inserted), 9, 1,
5, 3, 7 (right-hand overlapping number), 5, 6, 1, 2, 6 (7
already inserted). It will be possible to find other solutions.

38. (a) YES, by screwing 6 on upside down.

(b) Not without a saw.

39. (a) Several solutions are possible, but one example is:
    695
    782
    431

    or any combination of these numbers in the same columns.

    (b) 40.82
        9.75
        1.63
        ─────
        52.2
        ─────

40. Across

    A. 13824
    E. 16
    G. 405224
    H. 68121
    I. 9801
    L. 81
    M. 592704
    P. 64000
    Q. 2197
    R. 5625

    Down

    A. 10648
    B. 85184
    C. 44100
    D. 357911
    E. 125000
    F. 64
    J. 59319
    K. 17576
    L. 8464
    N. 7056
    O. 3025

41. MACMILLAN, PEDAL, BICYCLE (BICYCLE).
    LEVER, BAR, ROD (LEVERS).
    THATCHER, STRAW, ROOF (THATCHING).
    HOME, RESIDENCE, ABODE (WHERE WE LIVE).

42. CORSICA, ELBA, ST. HELENA (NAPOLEON).
    SARDINIA, CRETE, CYPRUS (MED. ISLANDS).
    ARGON, GALLIUM, XENON (ELEMENTS).
    ZEBU, ELAND, CHAMOIS (MAMMALS).

43. You should have grouped them in threes each totalling 1000.

44. MENDELSSOHN, ELIJAH, HEBRIDES
    (MENDELSSOHN).
    WESTERN ISLES, MINCH, STORNOWAY

(HEBRIDES).
ISRAEL, JAFFA, ASHDOD (ISRAEL).
HAYDN, CREATION, SEASONS (HAYDN).

45. TRAVELS, LILLIPUT, BROBDINGNAG
(GULLIVER).
SWIFT, SWALLOW, MIGRATION (BIRDS).
RAPID, QUICK, FAST (SPEED).
JOURNEY, EXCURSION, EXPEDITION (TRAVEL).

46. NILE, COPENHAGEN, AGAMEMNON (NELSON).
CONGO, NIGER, OBI (RIVERS).
OSLO, HELSINKI, STOCKHOLM (SCANDINAVIAN
CAPITALS).
KENYA, KAMET, ELIAS (MOUNTAINS).

47. TENT.

48. ENCIRCLE.

49. TENNIS.

50. BLINK.

51. COLONEL.

52. HIGH IQ.

53. DESPAIR.

54. WIRING.

55. BACKWARDSWAY.

56. UPSIDE DOWN.

Quotations Introduction anagram—William Shakespeare.

57. (a) All things come to him who will but wait—Longfellow.
Forget forgive conclude and be agreed—Shakespeare.

(b) Absence makes the heart grow fonder—Bayly.
The only way to have a friend is to be one—Emerson.

58. There is in the worst of fortune the best chances for a happy change—Euripides.

59. (a) The end of labour is to gain leisure—Aristotle.

   (b) A spark neglected makes a mighty fire—Herrick.

60. The only people who do not make mistakes are those who do nothing and that is the greatest mistake of all.

61. Your rewards for this effort are satisfaction and congratulations. Anagram: Nothing.

62. The square numbers are:

   Across—1296, 5184, 8649, 6241, 8464, 529, 2025, 1225, 49, 169, 36.
   Down—25, 16, 8281, 144, 1521, 256, 6889, 64, 4624, 9409, 576.

63. PRESTIDIGITATION.

64. Words are: MOP, END, COVET, SKYLIGHT, FRY, JIB, SQUAW, ZAX.

65.

7	13	4	10
2	12	5	15
9	3	14	8
16	6	11	1

66. When you successfully complete this puzzle you will have proved beyond doubt qualities of determination and patience.

67. $7 \times 4 \times 8 \times 6 \times 2 - 2 \times 6 \times 8 \times 8 - 768$
   82687   — 5376   — 630
   79988   — 36288   — 2304

68. 15707 — 3.1.44   — 20816
   17079 — 6.10.47 — 19444
   26632 — 1.12.73 — 9891

   The middle column is a date. The first column is the number of preceding days this century and the last column is the remaining days this century. The year 1900 was not a

121

leap year due to adjustments on the Gregorian Calendar, whereby the leap year is omitted at the turn of the century if the year is not divisible by 400, therefore, although 1900 was not a leap year, the year 2000 will be.

69. (f) each square contains three circles of differing sizes.

70. 1248 — 8 — 4096
    428 — 8 — 4096
    4812 — 8 — 4096

The product of the digits of each number in the first column is 64. The second column is the square root of 64. The third column is the square of 64.

71. (e)—in each vertical column the three words use the same four letters. The complete solution therefore is:

EDIT EMIR TIME
 | | |
TIDE RIME EMIT
 | | |
DIET MIRE MITE

72. (g)—(o = 1, T = 2) Magic 9 (each line, vertical, horizontal or diagonal, adds up to 9).

73. (f)—read each line both across and down to make a logical sequence. The complete solution is:

3261—3262—3263
 | | |
1623—2623—3623
 | | |
4884—5885—6886

N.B. 3261 + 1623 = 4884.

74. 3, 5, 6   —30 (Least common multiple)
    9, 15, 20   —180
    8, 9, 15, 16, 20—720

75. (b) (There are four concentric circles with their centre at the centre point of the middle square.)

76. 232 entries—229 matches were played, therefore there must

have been 229 losers. Add the two who scratched out without playing and then add the winner of the Championship and you arrive at the total number of entries—232.

77. Both one chance in four.

78. Remember pi to 8 decimal places. The number of letters in each word represents the digits of pi, i.e. 3.14159265.

79. 9 a.m.—to solve this puzzle you have to realise that if the clock strikes at 1-second intervals it only takes 10 seconds to strike 11 p.m. because it takes only 1 second for the first two strikes. Add 11 hours on to 11 p.m. i.e. 10 a.m. but then deduct 1 hour due to the clocks being put back at the end of British Summer Time and you arrive at the time of the appointment, 9 a.m.

80. Always four no matter how the grid is drawn.

81. He would pay slightly less. 1 inch square = *1 cu. in.* volume or 6 sq. in. area. 1.26 inch square cube = *2 cu. in.* volume or 9.5256 sq. in. area. To double the volume would require approximately 58.75 per cent increase in cardboard, i.e. the percentage increase from 6 to 9.5256. For every £100 worth of cardboard he would now have to pay £158.75, but the discount of 37.5 per cent on the new figure reduces the cost to £99.22.

82. 32—number the sides of the first cube 0,1,2,3,5,7. Number the sides of the second cube 0,1,2,4,6,8. The 6 can be turned over and displayed as a 9.

83. Circle most—triangle least.

84. (a) MISUNDERSTANDING.

(b) CIRCUMFERENCE.

85. O, NO, NOT, NOTE, TENOR, ORIENT, PROTEIN, INCEPTOR, RECEPTION.

86. SKY, JUMPY, QUARTZ, THONG, FOX, GLIB, VICE, DEW.

87. (a) ALTER—ALERT—LATER
(b) SEPAL—LEAPS—PLEAS
(c) REMIT—MITRE—TIMER
(d) SLIME—SMILE—MILES
(e) KILNS—SLINK—LINKS
(f) RESET—STEER—TREES

88. A, AT, ATE, LATE, LATER, RELATE, RELATED, RETAILED, LIBERATED, DELIBERATE.

89. (a) PALPITATE.

(b) SPINNAKER.

(c) CLOCKWISE.

(d) TEMPORARY.

(e) EXCURSION.

90. JOBS, OF, NYMPHS, ZYGAL, QUART, TWICE, KID, VEX.

91. (a) Queen Elizabeth, Spanish Armada defeated, back soon with treasure.   Francis Drake.

91. (b) Mark Antony, milkman delivered, please drop by tonight and scrub my back.   Cleopatra.

92. (a) V (vowel) 1 = A etc.   C (consonant) 1 = B etc. Well done! Message successfully decoded.

(b) A or N = 1,   B or O = 2 etc. To all the puzzle solvers who have persevered, patiently (?) to decode this message, congratulations!

93. The key is as follows:

A B C D E F G H I J K L M N O P Q R S T U V W X Y Z
| | | | | | | | | | | | | | | | | | | | | | | | | | |
M K Z H I O Q R A V T G Y W U F B C L X J D E S N P

Decoded, the message reads:

Trying to identify double letter words and common endings
such as 'ER' and 'ING' can be of considerable assistance
when attempting to decode messages of this type.
Additional information, for example, knowing that the letter
'E' is the most common letter in the English language and
that 'ING' is the most common three letter word ending is
also worth knowing.

94. (a) 6—look at a typewriter.

   (b) 7—to spell Morse Code.

95. (a) V for violet (colours of the rainbow).

   (b) C for Catherine Parr (Henry VIII's wives).

96. (a) Divides by 11 if the sum of alternate digits is equal.

   (b) R/NATIONALISATION.

   (c) $(14 + 3)(14 - 3) = 17 \times 11 = 187$.

97. Screw the threes together to make an eight.

98. (e)—the initial letters spell out P I C K S A I L.

99. GAS/SLAVE/LAS VEGAS. 'Las Vegas' uses the same
eight letters which appear in the words 'Gas' and 'Slave'.

100. NECKLACE.